SPRING

As winter ice begins to melt,

A little seed begins to sprout,

Sun softens the frosty ground,

First snowdrops peep out.

Snowdrop (Galianthus)

1

Gordon is nearly seven years old and loves
his dog Diggy.

Diggy and Gordon have lots of fun in Grandad's
garden. Grandad loves to work there with Gordon.

There is lots of digging, planting and growing, so they
get to eat yummy food.

It is spring and today they are preparing the ground
for this year's fruit and vegetables.

Diggy the dog is helping too!

Grandad loves to grow fruit and vegetables for Grandma.

Grandma loves to cook with Grandad's amazing apples and his very POLITE potatoes.

SUMMER

Picking potatoes in the sun,

Gordon and Grandad are tired, but it's fun.

The pea, carrot, tomato and spud

Picked from the garden,

the food will be good !

Courgette (Zucchini)

One beautiful sunny day Gordon and Grandad are basking in the sun and doing a little bit of gardening too.

It is summer and they are harvesting the potatoes.

Picking the spuds has made Grandad feel very tired.

'Sit down here with me' said Grandad. 'You did so well today! You are becoming a real gardener just as I reach the autumn of my life'.

'If I don't see next spring I would like you to keep my garden alive for me'.

'But Grandad', replied Gordon, 'what if you do not get to see next spring? I would miss you so much and anyway, who will show me what to do in the garden?'

'Don't worry Gordon, each time you don't know what to do or are feeling blue, think of me really, really hard and feel the MAGIC!'

Gordon is very sad to hear that Grandad may not be with him forever, but he is curious about this magic and asks loads of questions.

Grandad simply smiles and says 'Patience, dear Gordon, is a great virtue'.

AUTUMN

An apple grows upon a tree,

And then is picked for treats for tea.

For new life to grow, the old must be gone.

In our hearts, the memories live on.

Dahlia

Gordon wakes up. It is autumn and it is time to harvest some apples.

Hurrah, apples are amazing, they are SO tasty and he is very excited.

What will Grandma make with Grandad's apples?

Mmmm! Maybe some delicious apple crumble? Or stewed apple and custard?

Ohhh! he cannot wait.

(Fill me with autumn colour)

All of the apples have been harvested.
All of the leaves are gone from the trees
and Gordon and Grandad are having a lazy day.
They fall asleep in the warm evening sunshine.

Gordon is woken by the flutter of a very friendly
robin landing on his shoulder.

'Oh! How lovely!' He must tell Grandad.

Gordon tickles Grandad's nose but
Grandad does not wake up.

For Grandad, winter has come early and he will not see next spring.

Gordon and Grandma are very sad.

'Even though Grandad will no longer be with us Gordon, he will always be with us in our memories', said Grandma.

'I will think of him when I look into our beautiful garden and am so happy that you are here to look after Grandad's plants'.

WINTER

Under trees so bare through winter's frost,

Creatures huddle in their cosy cots.

There they will stay until the spring,

And dream of what the future will bring.

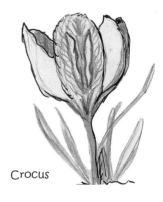

Crocus

12

Gordon likes to think about all the wonderful times
he had with Grandad.

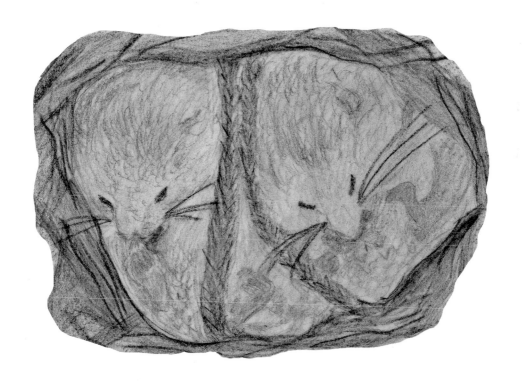

The little dozy dormice are having their
warm winter sleep.

SPRING

What's this note that Gordon has found?

It's from an old friend, the advice is sound.

But magic's afoot, where will it end?

Come with us now to Greenieland.

Snowdrop (Gallanthus)

One morning Gordon looks out and sees the snow is gone and there are Snowdrops coming up.

'Hurrah, it is spring!'

Gordon remembers how Grandad asked him to mind his garden. He gets straight to work!

But what should he do first? He thinks very hard about Grandad and suddenly he is by Grandad's shed, as if by MAGIC!

'Look! there is a plant with a note tied around it.

Why did I not notice this before?

I can't wait to get started'.

He runs excitedly to tell Grandma.

She gives Gordon a big kiss and says
'Breakfast first young man!'

This spot is perfect!

There is plenty of space, some shade, some sunshine,
and I will be able to water it every day.

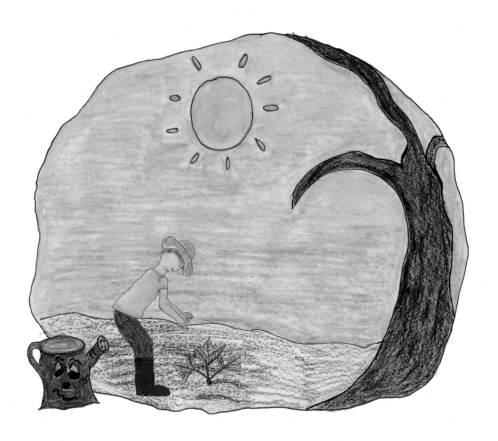

Gordon gently places the plant in the ground,
covers it with soil, and waters it with his
wibbly wobbly watering can.

Suddenly Gordon feels really GIDDY!

'I'm giddy as a GOAT!' he laughs.

He runs about the garden,

spinning round and round until he falls to the ground.

'Where am I?'

Diggy licks Gordon's nose and starts to bark excitedly.

'Oh Diggy, look at the ladybird! Is she really reading?'

Gordon smiles, this place feels SO special!

'C'mon Diggy let's go see!'

As Gordon walks he enjoys beautiful birdsong,
wonderful smells and sees the most amazing
colourful butterfly.

In the distance he sees somebody digging.

'I love his red wellies!'

'Oh I do too!' said Gordon, 'Grandad and I used to garden all the time'.

When your Grandad was a young boy, Gordon, we used to play here in GREENIELAND!

We learned such great things together'.

Gordon smiled, Grandad was GREAT!

Imagine, he played here with Greenie!

'Would you help me carry some wood for the fire?
It gets chilly on these spring evenings'.

As Gordon helps Greenie, he thinks warmly about
the fun times he had with Grandad.

Diggy has a good sniff and roll in the warm leaves.

He is one happy dog.

'This is wood from an ash tree I felled
in autumn' said Greenie.

'You felled it?'

'Yes, that means I chopped it down'.
Oh poor tree, thought Gordon.

'Don't worry' said Greenie, as if reading Gordon's mind,
'I was just about to plant a new ash tree
when you arrived.

It must be another ash as it is native to Ireland
and we must keep our Irish trees!'

'But why must we do that
Greenie?' asked Gordon.

'Trees are very,
very special.

They breathe in the nasty
gases from the air
and breathe out lovely
clean air'.

'We must make sure that our planet earth always
has enough trees' said Greenie.

'They provide shelter for animals
and help keep our air clean'.

'Oh, I had a hurley made from ash once' said Gordon.

'It was the best hurley ever and was really strong'.

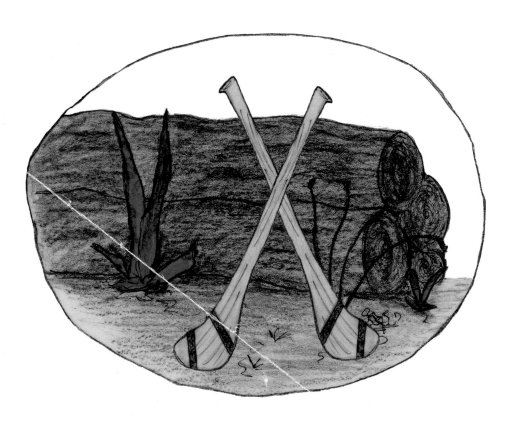

'What kind of animals live in an ash tree Greenie?'
asked Gordon.

Well there are forty one insects that live
in the ash tree!

Everything from beautiful birds,
to busy bugs and wiggly worms'.

'Look at my ash plant!' said Greenie.

'This spot is perfect;
there is shade and plenty of room'.

Those instructions sounded very familiar to Gordon.
They were the same as the ones on Grandad's note!

Greenie placed the plant
gently into the freshly dug
soil, covered it over and
gave it plenty of water.

As Greenie watered the plant
it grew and grew, as if by MAGIC!

Before he knew it Gordon was sheltered
by a beautiful ash tree and felt it was a
place where he could rest.

It had been such a long day.

Gordon and Diggy were feeling very, very sleepy.

He woke to the sound of his Grandmother.

'Gordon, come and have some dinner,

you've had a very busy day'.

THE END (for now)

NATURE Notes - Fraxinus excelsior

The ash (Fraxinus excelsior) is a native Irish tree, which grows to a height of 80 feet and has a life span of 200 years!

Grow it in a moist, cool place with partial shade and plenty of room. The ash is in leaf from April to October, flowering in April/May. It shows distinctive black leaf buds during the winter.

It produces bunches of pink/brown coloured 'keys' in autumn containing seeds, which are carried away by the wind from October onwards.

Ash has been used for making hurleys in Ireland for hundreds of years as it is tough, flexible, light and strong.

St. Patrick is said to have used an Ash stick to drive the snakes out of Ireland!

Fraxinus excelsior